# Tales Untold

## Rob Brannen

## Hodder & Stoughton

A MEMBER OF THE HODDER HEADLINE GROUP

# For Alice, Lydia and Maeve

## Acknowledgements

I am grateful to the staff and students at De Montfort University, Bedford, and particularly to Brigitte Doyle who worked with me on the first production of *Tales Untold*.

Above all, I am especially grateful for the fact that I am married to an excellent Drama teacher and want to thank Sharron for her support and guidance in all my work.

## Performance Rights

All rights whatsoever in these plays are strictly reserved, and professional and amateur applications for permission to perform them, etc., must be made in advance before rehearsals begin, to: Lucy Johnson, Hodder and Stoughton Educational, English and Drama Department, 338 Euston Road, London NW1 3BH.

Orders: please contact Bookpoint Ltd, 130 Milton Park, Abingdon, Oxon OX14 4SB. Telephone: (44) 01235 827720, Fax: (44) 01235 400454. Lines are open from 9.00–6.00, Monday to Saturday, with a 24 hour message answering service. Email address: orders@bookpoint.co.uk

British Library Cataloguing in Publication Data
A catalogue record for this title is available from The British Library

ISBN 0 340 75803 1

First published 1999
Impression number    10 9 8 7 6 5 4 3 2
Year                 2005 2004 2003 2002 2001

Cover photograph © Hugo Glendinning
Typeset by Fakenham Photosetting Ltd, Fakenham, Norfolk
Printed in Great Britain for Hodder & Stoughton Educational, a division of Hodder Headline Plc, 338 Euston Road, London NW1 3BH by The Bath Press Ltd.

# Contents

# INTRODUCTION

The eight plays in *Tales Untold* are based upon tales originally found in the brothers Grimm collection. Together they form a text designed to be performed by a young group or company. You may select one, a few, or all eight for performance, depending upon the context you are working in. The text can be used in a flexible way for your performance situation and group.

*Tales Untold* allows for:

1. a variable cast size with the possibility of multiple role-playing by all but those playing the central characters.
2. 'equal' roles without specific star parts with greater status
3. the strong possibility of more females than males in the cast, or
4. non gender-specific playing
5. performers' creative input through an 'open' text allowing for a sense of ownership and ensemble playing.

**Performance Exercises** and **Context Notes for the Performer** are included at the back of the text to kick-start the performance project.

# Prologue

Come quickly, come quickly someone is dreaming
Within their sleep, within their waking
Come quickly, come quickly a tale is emerging
A tale from the past, now worth the telling

Come and gather within this place
Observe our storytelling space
Unravel the thread, let the fable unfold
The tale no longer remains untold

Come quickly, come quickly the story is changing
Hold tight the beginning and twist hard the ending
Come quickly, come quickly these times are demanding
When morals mislead, the moral needs mending

Words lying deep in the long ago
Awake, rise up to the here and now
We shake off their dust and tell them anew
Now the dream, the nightmare, belongs to you

Come quickly, come quickly someone is dreaming
Within their sleep, within their waking
Come quickly, come quickly a tale is emerging
A tale from the past, now worth the telling

Come and gather within this place
Observe our storytelling space
Unravel the thread, let the fable unfold
The tale no longer remains untold

·1·

# Six Servants

## Cast List

| | |
|---|---|
| The Queen | Listener |
| The Princess | Tall One |
| The Prince | Shatter-Eyes |
| The King | Looker |
| Stout | Frosty-Hot |

| | |
|---|---|
| **Queen** | Long, long ago there lived a Queen whose heart was full of hatred. She was an old sorceress who had a wise and beautiful daughter. Day upon day, the Queen thought of nothing else but luring men to their doom. |
| **Princess** | Many, many, many men wanted to marry her daughter. |
| **Queen** | But before she would agree to any marriage, each suitor must perform a task set by the Queen. |
| **Princess** | Many, many, many men tried their luck . . . but all failed to perform the task set by the bitter, twisted, miserable old witch . . . my dear mother . . . who immediately made them kneel down and their heads were struck off. |
| **Queen** | Each day she lay in wait for the young men to come. 'Try if you must. I shall set three tasks for you. If you succeed, she is yours. If you fail then you will lose your life.' |
| **Prince** | In a land far away a Prince heard of the |

|        | Princess and said to his father: 'Let me go and try for her hand in marriage.' |
|--------|--------------------------------------------------------------------------------|
| King   | 'Never! If you go, you are as good as dead. No one has escaped so far; what makes you think you'll do any better? My love for you is too great. I could never let you go.' And at that the Prince fell gravely ill. Death hovered over his bed for seven long years. No physician could cure him, no doctor could revive him. Finally, his father reluctantly said: 'Go. Try to win the Princess if you must. I cannot help you in any other way.' |
| Prince | As soon as the Prince heard this, he immediately rose from his bed, his health completely restored, and he started happily on his way. |
| King   | Youngsters! What can you do? |
| Stout  | And the Prince travelled through hamlets, forests and farmland until the moment came when, looking into the distance, he saw something which resembled a large haystack – like this! . . . Nearer . . . a small mountain – like this! . . . Closer still, he saw that it was actually the belly of a man lying on the ground – like this! . . . The man said, 'Traveller, if you need a companion, take me.' |
| Prince | But what can I do with a big bloke like you? |
| Stout  | This? This is nothing. When I put my mind to it, I can expand to three thousand times my size – like this! |

| | |
|---|---|
| Prince | In that case I can use you. Come with me . . . and he began to tell of his mission. |
| Listener | So Stout joined the Prince and on they travelled until the moment came when they stumbled across someone lying down with an ear to the ground – like this. |
| Prince | What are you doing? |
| Listener | Listening. |
| Stout | What are you listening to? |
| Listener | I'm listening to an ant whispering secrets to her love, the beetle, and to the creaking of the grass as it grows through the soil. I've got extra special ears – they're large like this . . . and there is nothing I can't hear. |
| Prince | That's amazing! |
| Listener | That's nothing. I hear a fly in flight twenty miles away and heading in our direction. |
| Prince | In that case I can use you. If you want to be my companion, come along. |
| Listener | The Listener agreed to come along, and after a while the moment arrived when they came to a pair of feet. |
| Tall One | Then to a pair of legs which went on . . . and on . . . and on . . . – for they were as long as this! . . . After a while they reached a body and at last they reached a head. |
| Prince | Good fellow, you're as long as today and tomorrow! |
| Tall One | Oh that's nothing! When I really stretch out |

|  | I'm three thousand times as tall, as tall as the tallest tale – like this! |
|---|---|
| Prince | In that case, I can use you, come along. |
| Tall One | The Tall One joined them, and the four travelled on . . . |
| Shatter-Eyes | . . . until, upon a moment, they came across a man with bandages on his eyes. |
| Prince | Are your eyes so weak that you must hide them from the light? |
| Shatter-Eyes | No. My look is so sharp and so strong, that whatever I look upon is shattered to a thousand pieces. |
| Listener | Here comes that fly I was telling you about. |
| Shatter-Eyes | (lifting a corner of the bandage) Where? |

*The fly shatters into a thousand pieces*

| Prince | I can use you, Shatter-Eyes. If you wish to be our companion, come along. |
|---|---|
| Shatter-Eyes | (walking in the wrong direction) Shatter-Eyes joined them and . . . (they realise and guide him the right way) . . . Shatter-Eyes joined them and on they went . . . |
| Looker | . . . and suddenly the moment came when they saw someone craning a long neck to peer in many different directions – like this! |
| Prince | What are you looking at so intently? |
| Looker | I have eyes that are so sharp that I can see beyond the horizon to distant lands, over mountains and across the seas of the world, to |

pick out the tiniest detail. The eyebrow of a fly just shot past the tree tops over there a moment ago ... but I'm not sure why ...

**Shatter-Eyes**   Sorry.

**Prince**   Someone like you may be just what I need. Come along if you like.

**Looker**   After a while they saw a woman lying on the ground with the hot sun beating down on her ...

**Frosty-Hot**   ... but the woman was shivering and shaking − like this ... and her teeth were chattering and clattering − like this.

**Prince**   You poor little woman! On such a hot day, why are you so cold?

**Frosty-Hot**   Deary, deary me! I'm not like other folk. The hotter it is the more I shiver and shake, and the colder it is the more I sweat and swelter. In the hottest summer my bones are like ice. In the coldest winter I can't stand the heat!

**Prince**   That's amazing! And absolutely no use to anybody whatsoever. Come on you lot, let's go. (*He attempts to move off but the others stand their ground pleading with him.*) Oh all right then, she can come, (*as they move off*) but I don't know what the point of this frosty-hot, hot-frosty condition is ...

**Frosty-Hot**   The Prince led the way and the six companions followed.

**Stout**   Stout ...

**Listener**   The Listener ...

| | |
|---|---|
| **Tall One** | The Tall One . . . |
| **Shatter-Eyes** | Shatter-Eyes . . . |
| **Looker** | The Looker . . . |
| **Frosty-Hot** | . . . and Frosty-Hot. |
| **Prince** | Hey, Chatter-Teeth, keep up! . . . until finally they reached the Queen's country. |
| **Queen** | I have three tasks to set you. If you succeed in all of them you shall marry my daughter. First, bring to me a ring I once dropped in the Red Sea! |
| **Listener** | I can hear the lapping of the waves! This way! |
| **Looker** | And the Looker looked into the sea depths and said: 'There it is! Caught on a sharp stone!' |
| **Tall One** | I could reach the ring, if I could see it. |
| **Shatter-Eyes** | Shatter-Eyes looked at the sea and the strength of his look created a storm of huge waves! |
| **Stout** | Stout lay upon his enormous belly, opened his mouth wide and the waves tumbled into Stout as though poured into a bottomless pit. Glub. Glub. Glub. |
| **Looker** | He drank up the whole sea until its bed was as dry as a desert. |
| **Stout** | Oh dear! Oh dear! |
| **Shatter-Eyes** | Suddenly Stout desperately needed to fill the valley that he had created! |
| **Stout** | Oh dear! Oh dear! |

| | |
|---|---|
| **Tall One** | Without a moment to lose the Tall One stooped down into the depths of the valley. |
| **Stout** | Quickly! Quickly! |
| **Tall One** | And picked up the ring. Now Stout now! |
| **Shatter-Eyes** | With a great dam-burst the water returned. |
| **Stout** | (*with great relief*) Aaaaaaaaah ... |
| **Frosty-Hot** | Which is why it is not advisable to swim in the Red Sea. |
| **Prince** | The Prince found the ring ... |
| **Listener** | ... because – the Listener had listened ... |
| **Looker** | ... the Looker had looked ... |
| **Tall One** | ... the Tall One had reached ... |
| **Shatter-Eyes** | ... because of the strength of my look ... |
| **Stout** | ... and the size of my mouth! |

*They all look at Frosty-Hot*

| | |
|---|---|
| **Frosty-Hot** | And I ... I ... I'm very glad you found the ring. |
| **Prince** | Useless. I told you she'd be useless ... |
| **Queen** | (*begrudgingly*) Yes, it's the right ring. You've performed the first task. Now the second! Tonight I'll bring my daughter to your room. Hold her tight and don't fall asleep. I'll be there at midnight, and if she is not in your arms you will lose your life! |
| **Prince** | No problem! I shall stay awake all night and all day, if needs be. |

| | |
|---|---|
| Stout | Stout barred the door . . . |
| Looker | . . . and the Looker watched . . . |
| Prince | The Prince held the Princess and the moonlight shone through the window lighting up her beautiful face. The Prince had never been so happy. If only I could complete the three tasks and hold on to her forever. Eleven o'clock . . . only an hour to go . . . |
| Queen | At that moment the Queen cast a spell sending all of them to sleep and the Princess was carried away. |
| Princess | But the Queen, too sure of herself, had not made the spell strong enough, and at a quarter to twelve the magic wore off! |
| Prince | She's gone! All is lost, my Princess, my life, everything. (*He rages at Frosty-Hot*) Useless! Useless! Useless! |
| Listener | Quiet! Quiet! Listen. I can hear someone crying over there . . . |
| Looker | I can see the Princess trapped in a rock, three hundred miles north. |
| Tall One | The Tall One picked up Shatter-Eyes and within a few strides they were there. |
| Shatter-Eyes | Shatter-Eyes lifted his bandage for just one second and the rock shattered into a thousand pieces. |
| Queen | At the stroke of midnight the Queen came creeping into the Prince's chamber, sure that the Princess was encased inside a rock three |

hundred miles away. She was furious to discover the Princess safely in his arms ...

| | |
|---|---|
| **Listener** | ... because the Listener had listened ... |
| **Looker** | ... the Looker had looked ... |
| **Tall One** | ... the Tall One had taken mighty strides ... |
| **Shatter-Eyes** | ... Shatter-Eyes had blasted the rock ... |
| **Stout** | ... Stout had barred the door. |

*They all look at Frosty-Hot*

**Frosty-Hot**   And I ... I ... am very glad that the Princess is safe once more.

**Prince**   Useless. Useless. Going cold when it's hot and hot when it's cold, what is the point of that?

**Stout**   They turned to see a big bonfire had been built in front of the Queen's castle ...

**Shatter-Eyes**   Where?

**Queen**   'The third and final task! You cannot marry my daughter until someone agrees to sit in the middle of this bonfire and brave the flames.' The Queen knew that nobody could survive such a task. At last she would be rid of this persistent Prince and behead his freaky friends too!

**Prince**   Now I know that all our efforts have been in vain ...

**Listener**   My listening won't help ...

**Looker**   My looking won't help ...

**Tall One**   My size won't help ...

**Stout**          Nor mine . . .

**Shatter-Eyes**   My look would only engulf the entire
                   kingdom in flames . . .

**Prince**         No, for all your great powers my faithful
                   companions, there isn't a soul alive who could
                   sit at the centre of a raging bonfirè and survive.

*Slowly all heads turn to Frosty-Hot*

**Frosty-Hot**     'I'll have to wrap-up *really* warm' – said Frosty-
                   Hot, looking very pleased with herself . . .

·2·

# Clever Else

### Cast List

| | |
|---|---|
| The Father | Else |
| The Mother | The Maid |
| Hans | |

**Father**      I am the Father and I am thinking that it is time for our daughter, Clever Else, to get married.

**Mother**      I am the Mother and I am thinking the same as you. If only someone would have her!

**Else**      I am the daughter, Else, and I am thinking that is not such a good idea.

**Hans**      I am Hans and I am thinking: I am willing to marry Clever Else . . .

**Else**      I am thinking that is really not a good idea.

**Hans**      . . . but only if she is as clever as they say.

**Father**      I am saying she is so clever she can see wind coming up the street.

**Mother**      I am saying she is so clever she can hear flies coughing.

**Hans**      Then I am saying that is good . . . because if she is not clever, I won't take her.

**Else**      I am saying things don't look so good.

**All**      We are sitting having dinner.

| | |
|---|---|
| Father | ... making polite conversation ... |
| Mother | ... making plans for the future ... |
| Hans | ... making eyes at Else ... |
| Father, Mother & Hans | Clever, Clever Else. |
| Hans | I am thirsty. |
| Father | I am thirsty. |
| Mother | I am saying: Else go down to the cellar and get some beer. |
| Else | I am taking the beer jug and going down to the cellar to fetch some beer. I am setting it beside the beer barrel and turning the tap. I am looking up and I can see (*sudden horror*) a pickaxe lodged in the ceiling above my head, left by the builders! I am thinking what if I marry Hans and we have a little baby and when he grows up we send him down to the cellar to draw beer – that pickaxe will suddenly fall on his head and cut him in two! I am crying (*she does*). |
| Hans, Father & Mother | We are waiting. |
| Mother | I am calling: Maid! (*the Maid comes*) Go down to the cellar and see what's become of Else. |
| Maid | I am going down to the cellar to see what's become of Else. I am saying: Else, why are you crying? |
| Else | I am crying because if I marry Hans and we have a little baby and when he grows up we send him down to the cellar to draw beer, that |

|  | pickaxe (*Maid looks up in horror*) will suddenly fall on his head and cut him in two. |
| Maid | Clever Else! (*the Maid cries too*) |
| Hans, Father & Mother | We are waiting. |
| Father | I am saying: Wife, you had better go down to the cellar to see what's become of Else. |
| Mother | I am going down to the cellar to see what's become of Else. I am shocked: Else, why are you crying? |
| Else | I am crying about marrying Hans and having a little baby who will grow up and come down to draw beer and suddenly that pickaxe (*Mother looks up in horror*) will fall down and cut him in two. |
| Mother | Clever Else! (*starts crying too*) |
| Father & Hans | We are still waiting. |
| Father | I am very thirsty. |
| Hans | I am very thirsty. |
| Father | I am thinking that I had better go down to the cellar myself and see what's become of Else. (*Pointedly*) I am going down to the cellar myself to see what's become of Else. I am deafened by the wailing! And shouting: Else, why are you crying?! |
| Else | (*casual tone to the audience*) I am telling about Hans and the baby growing up and the drawing beer and that pickaxe (*Father looks up in horror*) that will cut him in two – you are knowing. |

| | |
|---|---|
| **Father** | Clever, Clever Else! (*cries too*) |
| **Hans** | (*after a pause*) I am waiting a long time now. I am very, very thirsty . . . and I am wondering what they are all up to. I am going down to the cellar to see what they are all up to. I am putting my hands over my ears and yelling: What terrible thing has happened?! |
| **Else** | I am heart-broken, Hans – if we marry and have a little baby who will grow up and come down to draw beer that pickaxe (*all look up in horror at the axe above Hans's head*) will suddenly fall and cut him in two. |
| **Hans** | I am crying . . . |

*Hans begins to sob. The others join in and the noise builds to wailing and screaming*

| | |
|---|---|
| **Hans** | . . . and the ground is rumbling . . . and the house is shaking . . . and the axe is falling and . . . |

*Hans falls dead*

*Silence*

| | |
|---|---|
| **Else** | Clever, Clever Else. |

## ·3·

# The Old Woman and Her Granddaughter

### Cast List

The Father          The Girl
The Mother          The Grandmother

*The scene is set and acted out by the family as the narration unfolds*

Father          There was once a very old woman. Coming to
                the end of her life, she now could hardly see
                and hardly hear. When she moved she would
                shake, as though she had been bitten hard by
                the winter winds.

Mother          (*impatiently*) Sitting at the table, she could
                hardly hold the spoon in her hand . . .

Father          The soup would spill upon the tablecloth . . .

Mother          . . . or run from the corner of her mouth.

Girl            The girl, her granddaughter, watched and
                played with some pieces of wood on the floor.

Father          The old woman's son . . .

Mother          . . . and his wife . . .

Father          . . . were repulsed by the old woman's
                behaviour and one day ordered her to sit
                behind the stove in the darkest corner, rather
                than offend their sight any longer.

Girl            All she was given to eat was some thin soup in
                a dirty little pot. From her place behind the
                stove, she would look upon the family table . . .

| | |
|---|---|
| **Grandmother** | . . . and her eyes would fill with tears. |
| **Girl** | The girl played with wood on the floor. |
| **Father** | One day, this old woman, tried to hold her pot in her trembly hands, but shook so much, she dropped it . . . |
| **Mother** | . . . the little clay pot fell to the floor and smashed, and the mother was furious. |
| **Girl** | My Grandmother only sighed and said nothing. |
| **Father** | From then on she had to eat out of an old tin pan. |
| **Girl** | The girl continued to play with pieces of wood until one day her Father said . . . |
| **Father** | My daughter, what are you doing? |
| **Girl** | I'm making a trough, Father, so that when I'm big and strong, you and mother can eat out of it. |

*Pause. Father and Mother look at each other. They go to the corner and bring the Grandmother back to the table and give her a clean bowl*

| | |
|---|---|
| **Girl** | Grandmother ate with us from then on, and when she spilt a little soup . . . (*she does*) . . . nothing was said. |

*Nothing is said*

·4·

# The Shoes That Were Danced Through

*This story is predominantly told through movement with various players/characters taking alternate lines of text. The lines, as printed here, and the stage directions are to help the company explore the movement/dance possibilities the narrative presents.*

*Generally each new line should be taken by a different voice. A group of lines in bold should be taken by the same player. Where there is a / in the middle of a line, the delivery of the following line should begin at this point. When this is the case, the next voice will begin delivery as the previous voice finishes speaking, so that the lines, when spoken, overlap.*

A King had twelve daughters
Twelve precious daughters
Each night he locked them in their room
Twelve beds, side by side
And in/ the morning
And in/ the morning
And in/ the morning
Their shoes were danced through

(*The King steps forward*)

**How can this be? Who will find out?**
**Three days to solve the mystery**
**Succeed and the kingdom is yours**
**Fail and you lose your life**

(*A Prince volunteers*)

**I shall keep watch**
**I will observe, discover, find out**

**To solve the mystery**
**Why the shoes are worn out**

(*The Prince takes his position, and the Princesses approach*)

Some wine before bed
To soothe
To calm
To salute the dark night

(*The Prince drinks the wine. He battles with tiredness before finally falling asleep*)

And in/ the morning
And in/ the morning
And in/ the morning
Their shoes were danced through

The second night
To soothe
To calm
Salute the dark night
Their shoes were danced through

The third night
Soothe
Calm
The dark night
Their shoes were all completely danced through

And the Prince was the first of many to lose his life

Finally a poor soldier came to town
Giving what little money he had
To a poor beggar woman
If only she knew how to solve the mystery

**Do not drink the wine offered to you**
**This leads all to the deepest slumber**

**Wear this enchanted cloak**
**And you will become – invisible!**

Three days to solve the mystery

(*The Soldier is offered the wine*)

To soothe
To calm
To salute the dark night

(*He pretends to drink and to fall asleep*)

(*The Princesses open cupboards, chests and boxes, taking out splendid clothes. They prepare themselves excitedly, looking in their mirrors. When they are all ready, the eldest taps on her bed and it sinks into the ground revealing the entrance to a tunnel*)

The bed sinks
Into the bedroom floor
A tunnel is revealed
And the sisters descend
The Soldier once cloaked
Becomes invisible!

(*The Soldier puts on his cloak and follows them underground. Invisible, he interacts with the Princesses, but they look straight through him*)

Deeper, deeper underground
Down, down, under the ground
Until, finally, the tunnel leads
To a brightly lit palace
Where twelve Princes await
Their dancing partners

(*The Princesses and Princes dance, and the soldier dances unseen*)

Spiral
Spinning
Swirling

Long into/ the night
Long into/ the night
Long into/ the night
Until ...
Their shoes were danced through

The second night
Twisting
Turning
Twirling
Their shoes were danced through

The third night
Spiral
Spin
Swirl

(*The movement qualities are repeated, but become more frantic. The Soldier
becomes increasingly enchanted by, and involved in, the dance sequence*)

Their shoes were all completely danced through!

(*Sudden stillness. Silence. The King steps forward*)

**Where have my daughters been dancing each night
And worn away their shoes to holes with tattered lace?**

(*The Soldier steps forward*)

**I have observed, I followed
I have discovered
I have solved the mystery
A goblet from the palace where they dance**

(*A goblet is revealed. The Princesses are shocked*)

Never more to dance
To be held by my prince
Never more
Spiral

Spinning
Swirling
Long into the night
And dance our shoes through

**Tell me where**
**And I will spare your life**
**The kingdom will be yours**
**And a princess for your wife**

(*The Soldier looks at the Princesses*)

Never more/ to dance
Never/ more
Never/ more
Never/ more
In the arms/ of my prince
Into the night
To dance our shoes through

(*The Soldier puts on his cloak . . .* )

Seize him! He must tell or die!

(*. . . and he becomes invisible*)

This way!
No this way!

The Soldier walked through them
Unseen
And deep within he carried
The secret
Of the shoes that were danced through

# ·5·

# The Stolen Pennies

## Cast List

| | |
|---|---|
| The Visitor | The Father |
| The Mother | The Child |

**Visitor**   It so happened that a man was sitting down to dinner with his wife and a friend who had come to visit.

**Mother**   They were talking and eating when the clock struck twelve ...

**Visitor**   And the visitor saw the door open and a pale child came in. Without a word or a look, this child walked straight into the next room. Several minutes passed, and in the same silent manner as before, the child walked back through the room, and was gone. The second day ... (*the clock strikes and the child does the same*) ... and the third day (*the clock strikes and the child does the same*)

**Father**   Finally the visitor turned to the father and said ...

**Visitor**   Whose child is it that comes everyday at noon, and goes into the next room?

**Father**   Child?

**Visitor**   The child who walks through here everyday and goes into the next room.

**Father**   I have seen no child.

*The clock strikes*

| | |
|---|---|
| Visitor | There she is, walking in the same way as before. |
| Father | What child? |
| Mother | There's nobody there. |
| Visitor | The visitor stood and went to the door of the next room. He opened it just enough for him to peer inside, and there was the child sitting on the floor … |
| Child | (*slowly and deliberately*) … clawing with its fingers … digging into the cracks … between the floorboards … looking … looking … |
| Visitor | Suddenly the child sensed his watching eyes and upon catching sight of the visitor … |
| Child | The child vanished. |
| Visitor | The visitor told the others what had happened and described the child … |
| Mother | Then the mother knew who it was: my little child died four weeks ago. |
| Father | They tore up the floorboards and there they discovered … |
| Mother | … two pennies that the mother had once given to the child for a poor man … |
| Mother/Child | (*together*) … the child had thought to herself, I shall buy myself some cake instead … |
| Mother/Child/ Father | (*together*) … keeping the pennies for herself, she hid them under the floorboards … |

| | |
|---|---|
| **Child** | And after death . . . |
| **Mother/Child/** **Father/Visitor** | (*together*) . . . the child could find no rest in the grave and returned every day at noon searching for the hidden money . . . |
| **Child** | . . . looking . . . looking . . . searching . . . searching . . . |
| **Visitor** | The parents took the pennies and gave them to a poor man and the child has not been seen since. |

# ·6·

# Six Stupid Hans

## Cast List

| | |
|---|---|
| The Mother | Hans 4 |
| Hans 1 | Gretal |
| Hans 2 | Hans 5 |
| Hans 3 | Hans 6 |

**Mother**    There was once a woman who had six sons, and all six sons were called Hans ... Which at times led to some confusion ...

**Hans 1**    Hans! Not you Hans, Hans.

**Hans 2**    Me Hans?

**Hans 3**    Me Hans?

**Hans 4**    Me Hans?

**Hans 1**    No, Hans.

**All Other Hans**    Oh Hans!

**Hans 3**    We thought you meant Hans ...

**Mother**    Now all of my sons loved one girl called Gretal, who lived at the neighbouring farm. Where are you going, Hans?

**Hans 1**    To see Gretal.

**Mother**    Good luck, Hans!

**Hans 1**    Sure thing. Bye, mother.

**Mother**    Bye, Hans.

| | |
|---|---|
| Hans 1 | Afternoon, Gretal. |
| Gretal | Afternoon, Hans. What have you brought me? |
| Hans 1 | Brought nothing. You give something. |
| Gretal | I'll give you a . . . needle. |
| Hans 1 | A needle? |
| Gretal | A needle. |
| Mother | Evening Hans. |
| All Other Hans | Evening! |
| Mother | This Hans! Where have you been? |
| Hans 1 | Been to see Gretal. |
| Mother | What did you bring her? |
| Hans 1 | Brought nothing. She gave. |
| Mother | What did she give you? |
| Hans 1 | Gave a needle. |
| Mother | What did you do with the needle, Hans? |
| Hans 1 | Stuck it safely in a bail of hay. |
| Mother | Was that clever Hans? |
| All Other Hans | No! |
| Mother | That was foolish, Hans. You should have stuck it in your sleeve. |
| Hans 2 | A-ha! |
| Hans 1 | (*Trying to find needle*) Oh dear. |
| Mother | Where are you going, Hans? |
| Hans 2 | To see Gretal, mother. |

| | |
|---|---|
| Mother | Good luck, Hans. |
| Hans 2 | Sure thing. Bye, mother. |
| Mother | Bye, Hans. |
| Hans 2 | Afternoon, Gretal. |
| Gretal | Afternoon, Hans. What have you brought me? |
| Hans 2 | Brought nothing. You give something. |
| Gretal | I'll give you a . . . knife. |
| Hans 2 | A knife? |
| Gretal | A knife. |
| Mother | Evening Hans. |
| All Other Hans | Evening! |
| Mother | This Hans! Where have you been? |
| Hans 2 | Been to see Gretal. |
| Mother | What did you bring her? |
| Hans 2 | Brought nothing. She gave. |
| Mother | What did she give you? |
| Hans 2 | Gave a knife. |
| Mother | What did you do with the knife, Hans? |
| Hans 2 | Stuck it in sleeve. |
| Mother | Was that clever, Hans? |
| All Other Hans | No! |
| Mother | That was foolish, Hans. You should have put it carefully in the back of your trousers. |
| Hans 3 | A-ha! |

| | |
|---|---|
| Hans 2 | (*Examining cut shirt*) Oh dear. |
| Mother | Where are you going, Hans? |
| Hans 3 | To see Gretal, mother. |
| Mother | Good luck, Hans. |
| Hans 3 | Sure thing. Bye, mother. |
| Hans 3 | Afternoon, Gretal. |
| Gretal | Afternoon, Hans. What have you brought me? |
| Hans 3 | Brought nothing. You give. |
| Gretal | I'll give you a . . . goat. |
| Hans 3 | A goat! |
| Gretal | A goat. |
| Mother | Evening Hans. |
| All Other Hans | Evening! |
| Mother | This one! Where have you been? |
| Hans 3 | Been to see Gretal. |
| Mother | What did you bring her? |
| Hans 3 | Brought nothing. She gave. |
| Mother | What did Gretal give you? |
| Hans 3 | Gave goat. |
| Mother | And what . . . have you done . . . with the goat? |
| Hans 3 | Put it carefully down the back of my trousers. |
| Mother | Was that clever Hans? |
| All other Hans | No! |

| | |
|---|---|
| Mother | That was foolish, Hans. You should have put a rope around its neck and led her home. |
| Hans 4 | A-ha! |
| Hans 3 | (*Looking down his trousers*) Oh dear. |
| Mother | Where are you going, Hans? |
| Hans 4 | To see Gretal, mother. |
| Mother | Good luck, Hans. |
| Hans 4 | Sure thing. Bye mother. Afternoon, Gretal. |
| Gretal | What have you brought me? |
| Hans 4 | Brought nothing. You give. |
| Gretal | I'll give you a . . . piece of bacon. |
| Hans 4 | A piece of bacon! |
| Gretal | Yes. Bacon. |
| Mother | Evening Hans. |
| All Other Hans | Eve . . . |
| Mother | THIS! . . . Hans . . . Where have you been? |
| Hans 4 | Been to see Gretal. |
| Mother | What did you bring her? |
| Hans 4 | Brought nothing. She gave. |
| Mother | What did Gretal give you? |
| Hans 4 | Gave bacon. |
| Mother | Bacon! Big bacon? (*Hans 4 nods*) Enough to feed a mother and her six sons called Hans big bacon? (*Hans nods again*) What did you do with the bacon, Hans? |

| | |
|---|---|
| **Hans 4** | Tied a rope round it, dragged it home, dogs came . . . and took away. |
| **Mother** | Was that clever, Hans? |
| **All Other Hans** | No! No! |
| **Mother** | That was foolish, Hans. You should have carried the bacon on your head. |
| **Hans 5** | A-ha! |
| **Hans 4** | (*Examining the rope with nothing on it*) Oh dear. |
| **Mother** | Where are you going, Hans? |
| **Hans 5** | To see Gretal, mother. |
| **Mother** | Good luck, Hans. |
| **Hans 5** | Sure thing. Bye, mother. |
| **Mother** | Bye, Hans. |
| **Hans 5** | Afternoon, Gretal. |
| **Gretal** | Afternoon, Hans. What have you brought me? |
| **Hans 5** | Brought nothing. You give something. |
| **Gretal** | I'll give you a . . . hog. |
| **Hans 5** | A hog!? |
| **Gretal** | Yes, a hog. |
| **Mother** | Evening, Hans. |
| **All Other Hans** | A very good evening to you, our mother, who has fed and nurtured us since we were tiny babies in your arms. (*The mother looks at them in despair*) |
| **Mother** | This one, where have you been? |

| | |
|---|---|
| **Hans 5** | Been to see Gretal. |
| **Mother** | What did you bring her? |
| **Hans 5** | Brought nothing. She gave. |
| **Mother** | What did Gretal give you? |
| **Hans 5** | Gave hog. |
| **Mother** | What did you do with the hog, Hans? |
| **Hans 5** | Put it on head, kicked face, made mess in hair. |
| **Mother** | Was that clever, Hans? |
| **All Other Hans** | Nooooooo! |
| **Mother** | That was foolish, Hans. You should have held it tightly under your arm, taken it to the pig sty and dropped it in the mud. |
| **Hans 6** | A-ha! |
| **Other Hans** | Uh-oh. |
| **Hans 5** | (*Rubbing his hair and examining it*) Oh dear. |
| **Mother** | Where are you going, Hans? |
| **Hans 6** | To see Gretal, mother. |
| **Mother** | Go on then, just go. |
| **Hans 6** | Afternoon, Gretal. |
| **Gretal** | Afternoon, Hans. What have you brought me? |
| **Hans 6** | Brought nothing. You give something. |
| **Gretal** | Nothing left, Hans. I'll come home with you. |
| **Hans 6** | Oh good. |

*He picks her up, carries her to the pig sty and drops her in the mud*

| | |
|---|---|
| **Mother** | Hans, what are you doing with Gretal? |
| **Hans 6** | Held her tight, took her to the sty and dropped her in the mud. |
| **Mother** | Was that clever, Hans? |
| **All other Hans** | No! No! No! |
| **Hans 1** | Yes! (*The others look at him*) No . . . No . . . No . . . Not at all clever . . . |
| **Mother** | That was very foolish, Hans, and no way to treat the girl you want to marry. You should have given her the eye. |
| **Hans** | All right, mother. |

*He pulls out one of his eyes . . .*

| | |
|---|---|
| **Hans 6** | Aowh! |

*. . . and gives it to Gretal*

| | |
|---|---|
| **Gretal** | Eventually, Gretal married . . . a man called . . . Ludwig . . . Which is not surprising, really, is it? |

·7·

# Eve's Children

## Cast List

| | |
|---|---|
| God | Eve |
| Handsome | Filthy |
| Pretty | Grubby |
| Delightful | Scabby |
| Sweetness | Dog-Breath |
| Neat | Blot |
| Tidy | Spotty |

**God**      In this story I play the part of God. Please use your imaginations as freely as you wish. When I sent Adam and Eve out of Paradise, they had to build their house on barren land, toil for their food, make clothes for themselves, and life was generally hard. But we all have to live with our mistakes.

**Eve**      Eve had twelve children with her husband, Adam ... six handsome ones ... (*they enter*) and six ugly ones. (*they enter*)

**Filthy**      Those of us playing the ugly ones in this story would like to point out that we are only pretending to be ugly and that these roles are testing our acting ability to the full.

**Handsome**      Those of us playing handsome ones have been specifically chosen for these roles which come quite naturally to us.

*The two groups glare at each other*

| | |
|---|---|
| Eve | Children! Children! I have received a message from an angel. God is coming to look at our household to see how we're getting on and to bless my children. *(She instructs the handsome children)* Handsome, comb your hair and stand here, Pretty put on your best dress and stand here, Delightful, here, holding these flowers, Sweetness, wash and sit here, Neat and Tidy, best jackets on, standing there and there. Good, all sorted! *(She turns to the ugly children)* Oh . . . |
| Filthy | What about us, mother? |
| Eve | Yes . . . well . . . I really want you to help me children so . . . Filthy, down to the cellar and scrape each brick clean with your fingernails . . . Grubby, up to the attic, take each cobweb down and put them in separate boxes . . . Scabby, go to the barn and place each piece of straw in order of length . . . Dog-Breath, groom the billy goat and spin its hair into twelve balls of wool for your next jumper . . . Blot, wash Dog-Breath's underwear in the pig trough until it smells of roses . . . and Spotty, climb up the chimney to stop any draft coming down and giving Our Lord a chill . . . *(There is a knock at the door)* Go! |

*The Uglies leave and the Handsome ones get into position just in time as God enters*

| | |
|---|---|
| Eve | Oh God! I mean . . . oh, God, how honoured we are to have you call round and bless my children. |

*God wanders round inspecting the house and the Handsome children bow and curtsey*

| | |
|---|---|
| **God** | Are these your children? |
| **Eve** | Yes, Lord. |
| **God** | Very nice. (*Blessing the children*) You, you will be a mighty monarch. You will be a prince and you, a countess. You, a fine lady in silks, and you, a great scholar. You, there, will be a wealthy merchant. |
| **Eve** | Rich blessings on them all! The Lord certainly is in a generous mood. I shall fetch my other children to be blessed! From the cellar, the attic, the barn, the stable, the sty and the chimney . . . (*The Uglies all assemble*) Er, Lord, just before you go . . . I'd almost forgotten about these, my other children . . . |
| **God** | Oh . . . well . . . I will give these too my blessing . . . You will be a woodcutter. You, a peasant. You, a farmer's hand. You, a soldier. You, a peasant's wife with fourteen children, and you, a domestic servant all the days of your life. |

*God is about to leave*

| | |
|---|---|
| **Eve** | Pardon me, Lord, but how can you give out such unequal blessings? These are all my children, I gave birth to each one. Should you not give equal blessings? |
| **God** | Eve, you don't understand. If I made them all royalty and nobles, who would grow the grain? Who would chop the wood? Who would bring up the children? Who would fight |

|          | the wars? Each one to their place. Such is the way of the world, where one is sustained by the other. |
|----------|----------|
| **Eve**  | Forgive me, Lord. I spoke in haste. Your will be done. |
| **God**  | . . . and that would be the end of this story only the one playing Grubby whispered . . . |
| **Grubby** | . . . but I want to be a scholar . . . to learn of the highest mountains, of the deepest oceans, of people and places unknown, to tell the secrets of the universe . . . |
| **God**  | . . . so perhaps it was only the beginning. |

# ·8·

# Twelve Sisters

## Cast List

| | |
|---|---|
| Sarah | Sister 3 |
| The Mother | Sister 4 |
| The Chorus | (and seven other sisters) |
| Sister 1 | A Witch |
| Sister 2 | The Brother |

*A mother sits and weeps*

**Sarah**      Mother, Queen, why are you so sad?

**Mother**      Sarah, you are no longer to be my youngest child. I am to have another.

**Sarah**      But, my Mother, my Queen, why are you so sad?

**Mother**      I have twelve daughters. If my thirteenth child is a boy the King has said that my daughters must die. Then the boy shall inherit a great wealth and he alone will rule this kingdom.

**Chorus**      *Twelve coffins in a row*
*Waiting for an occupant*
*A child to be his father's joy*
*And a mother's lament*
*And a mother's lament*
*A boy his father's joy*
*And a mother's lament*

**Sarah**      Mother, dry all your tears. We can take care of ourselves. Your daughters will run away together.

| | |
|---|---|
| Mother | Run to the forest with your eleven sisters. By turns keep watch. If I give birth to a girl, I shall raise a white flag and you may return home. But upon the birth of a boy, the red flag shall fly. Then run, run to save your lives. Every single night I shall think of you and your sisters. I will pray in the winter you find wood for a fire and in the summer that you find fresh water to cool you in the heat. |
| Chorus | *Twelve coffins in a row*<br>*Twelve pillows at the head*<br>*White to welcome daughters home*<br>*The danger signal's red*<br>*The danger signal's red*<br>*White will welcome daughters home*<br>*The danger signal's red* |
| Sarah | For eleven days and nights they watched, until ... on the twelfth day when I took my turn – My mother is raising a flag ... and the flag is ... red! |

*The sisters run*

| | |
|---|---|
| Sarah | Deeper into the forest ... |
| Sister 1 | Where shall we live? |
| Sarah | Deeper into the forest ... |
| Sister 2 | What shall we eat? |
| Sarah | Deeper into the forest ... |
| Sister 3 | Who will protect us? |
| Sarah | Deeper into the forest ... |
| Sister 4 | Who will provide for us? |

*A witch appears*

| | |
|---|---|
| **Witch** | Why are you running sisters? |
| **Chorus** | *Our father has the boy he loves*<br>*For us twelve coffins in a row*<br>*Upon the meeting of a man*<br>*We swear his blood will flow*<br>*We swear his blood will flow*<br>*No man is safe within our sight*<br>*We swear his blood will flow* |
| **Witch** | Then this is your promise. You may live in my house as long as you wish. But if you talk to a man your promise is broken, and a broken promise will bring nothing but harm. |
| **Sarah** | We lived in the witch's house, deep within the forest . . . |
| **Sister 1** | . . . and learnt how to hunt for our food . . . |
| **Sister 2** | . . . how to build our fires . . . |
| **Sister 3** | . . . how to cook the meats . . . |
| **Sister 4** | . . . and fruits of the forest. |
| **Sarah** | Many, many years passed, until one day . . . |

*The Brother enters the forest*

| | |
|---|---|
| **Sister 1** | A man . . . |
| **Sister 2** | . . . a man . . . |
| **Sister 3** | A man comes this way . . . |
| **Sister 1** | Remember our promise . . . |
| **Sister 2** | . . . do not speak . . . |
| **Sister 3** | . . . his blood must flow. |

| | |
|---|---|
| Chorus | *I have seen twelve coffins in a row*<br>*Having thought I was alone*<br>*And now I roam my father's land*<br>*For the sisters never known*<br>*For the sisters never known*<br>*My mother told the fearful fate*<br>*Of the sisters never known* |
| Sisters | Brother! |
| Witch | Oath renounced. Promise broken. |
| Sarah | Upon speaking to their brother the twelve sisters were turned into ravens and flew away over the tree tops. |
| Witch | Because they spared your life, your sisters have been changed into ravens forever. |
| Brother | Is there any way of saving them? |
| Witch | There is only one way to break the spell but that is far too difficult. |
| Brother | What must I do? |
| Witch | You cannot hope to succeed . . . |
| Brother | What must I do? |
| Witch | . . . too difficult . . . |
| Brother | What? |
| Witch | Stay silent for seven long years. You must not speak, or laugh or cry out. One word from your mouth, or even the slightest whimper and your sisters will fall from the sky, and twelve dead ravens will lie at your feet. |
| Brother | Then this is my promise – for seven years I |

|             |                                                                                                                                                                                                                                                                                                                                                                                                                                                    |
| ----------- | -------------------------------------------------------------------------------------------------------------------------------------------------------------------------------------------------------------------------------------------------------------------------------------------------------------------------------------------------------------------------------------------------------------------------------------------------- |
|             | will remain in silence to annul this spell upon my sisters.                                                                                                                                                                                                                                                                                                                                                                                         |
| Mother      | My son wandered the earth, a mute beggar, from village to village, scorned and abused. He could not plead for charity, he could not cry out when beaten. People wondered at the secrets he was hiding and the thoughts he never voiced. Time passed, and not one single sound had passed his lips. Then, walking in a wood, someone approached . . . The King, his father, separated from his hunting party and watching something flying overhead. |
| Sisters     | Ravens!                                                                                                                                                                                                                                                                                                                                                                                                                                             |
| King        | The Hunter-King took an arrow from his quiver, raised his bow from his side, and just for sport took aim at the smallest, blackest raven.                                                                                                                                                                                                                                                                                                            |
| Mother      | The brother was about to cry out . . .                                                                                                                                                                                                                                                                                                                                                                                                              |
| Sister 1    | Swooping down . . .                                                                                                                                                                                                                                                                                                                                                                                                                                 |
| Sister 2    | . . . from the skies . . .                                                                                                                                                                                                                                                                                                                                                                                                                          |
| Sister 3    | . . . a flock of ravens . . .                                                                                                                                                                                                                                                                                                                                                                                                                       |
| Sister 4    | . . . gouging eyes                                                                                                                                                                                                                                                                                                                                                                                                                                  |
| Sister 1    | Pecking . . .                                                                                                                                                                                                                                                                                                                                                                                                                                       |
| Sister 2    | . . . clawing . . .                                                                                                                                                                                                                                                                                                                                                                                                                                 |
| Sister 3    | . . . tearing flesh . . .                                                                                                                                                                                                                                                                                                                                                                                                                           |
| Sister 4    | Sent the King . . .                                                                                                                                                                                                                                                                                                                                                                                                                                 |
| Sister 1    | . . . to eternal rest.                                                                                                                                                                                                                                                                                                                                                                                                                              |
| Mother      | The cry went out 'Our King is murdered!'                                                                                                                                                                                                                                                                                                                                                                                                            |

| | |
|---|---|
| Witch | Our King is dead! |
| Sarah | Twelve ravens circle overhead. |
| Witch | (*to the Brother*) Murderer! Condemned to die! |
| Mother | My son? It is the lost prince! |
| Witch | Too eager to inherit the kingdom, he stole it from his father's hands. |
| Mother | Speak, my son, proclaim your innocence. (*He remains silent*) Speak! Speak to save your life and your mother's heart from breaking. |

*Silence*

| | |
|---|---|
| Witch | A life for a life. A murderer must die. |

*The execution is prepared*

| | |
|---|---|
| Mother | (*softly*) Speak . . . |

*He is about to be executed as . . .*

| | |
|---|---|
| Sister 1 | Twelve ravens from on high . . . |
| Sister 2 | Twelve ravens swooping down . . . |
| Sister 3 | Twelve ravens change in shape and form . . . |
| Sister 4 | Twelve sisters touch the ground. |
| Mother | The last second of seven silent years had passed, the sisters returned and their brother spoke: |
| Brother | *Twelve coffins in a row*<br>*Remain behind locked door*<br>*Testament to my father's crime*<br>*Shall be empty evermore*<br>*Shall be empty evermore* |
| Sarah | A tale untold shall now have voice<br>Twelve coffins . . . empty . . . for evermore. |

# PERFORMANCE MATERIALS

Employ a selection of simple props or materials to illustrate the stories in an open style. The only materials used for the original production were:

5 sheets of canvas (5′ × 5′)

Various lengths of thick wooden doweling 'sticks'

The canvas sheets had triangular pockets sewn into the corners which allowed for sticks to be inserted into them for various effects. For example, the end of one 5′ stick into one pocket and the canvas can be waved like a flag, or four 5′ sticks with their ends inserted in the pockets can create a ridged square, becoming a wall or a door.

Choose your own materials: lengths of rope, strips of coloured cloth, boxes, cartwheels, sandbags etc. Once the rules of the game are established (in our case: using only sticks, sheets and your own bodies) then the participants are free to play.

# PERFORMANCE EXERCISES

These exercises attempt to empower the performance group to think creatively and collectively at the beginning of the project. The first two establish a performance style. The third applies this style to some of the 'impossible' moments from the text. The fourth should encourage sound ideas for effects (e.g. the wind) and for atmospherics (e.g. an eerie rhythm). Ideas which arise from these last two exercises can be incorporated into the performance during rehearsal.

## Bodies and Props

### Exercise A

In groups of five or six use only your bodies to create:

1. An object or machine or piece of furniture found in the living room

2. Something found in the bedroom
3. Something found or used in the garden
4. A mode of transport

All the participants are either a part of the 'something' being made (e.g. the wheel of a motorbike) or demonstrating how it is used (e.g. the rider of a motorbike made up of five other people).

**Exercise B**
Repeat the above exercise but now you can use the production materials as well as your bodies.

**Exercise C**
Label your groups A to E. Using only the members of your group (5 or 6) and the production materials provided create:

### Group A
1. The fattest person in the world
2. Someone descending to a cellar
3. Someone hiding up a chimney

### Group B
1. The tallest person
2. A secret door leading to a maze of corridors
3. A marionette show*

### Group C
1. The Ocean – that is drained, then returns
2. Ripping up the floorboards of a house and finding a magic coin
3. Running through a deep, dark forest

### Group D
1. Someone trapped inside a rock which is shattered to pieces
2. A dog chasing a piece of bacon being pulled along
3. A bird flying over the tree tops

### Group E
1. Someone sitting down at a dinner table
2. A very muddy pigsty
3. An execution

\* The original cast member Sarah Funnell contributed the idea of playing the story of *Six Stupid Hans* with all the characters as marionettes. The idea was so successful that I would recommend it as a consideration.

## Props and Sound Exercise
Using only the production materials and your own voices, how can sound be used to enhance the following excerpts?:
1. 'The Prince held the Princess and the moonlight shone through the window lighting up her beautiful face. The Prince had never been so happy. If only I could complete the three tasks and hold on to her forever.'
2. Spiral
   Spinning
   Swirling
   Long into/ the night
   Long into/ the night
   Long into/ the night
   Until …
   Their shoes were danced through
3. … the clock struck twelve … And the visitor saw the door open and a pale child came in. Without a word or a look, this child walked straight into the next room. Several minutes passed, and in the same silent manner as before, the child walked back through the room and was gone.

## Storytelling Exercises
Recognise the three styles of playing incorporated into the telling of these stories:
1. Naturalistic
   For example dialogue between the Mother and Sarah at the

beginning of *Twelve Sisters*. Here the audience is eavesdropping upon their conversation.

2. Direct Address

   For example, the Queen opens *Six Servants* in character but her lines are those of a storyteller addressing the audience. Here the audience is the Queen's confidant. She is entrusting it with this information and so draws it in by her delivery.

3. Self-referential

   This is where the actor acknowledges her/himself as an actor to the audience. An obvious example of this comes at the beginning of *Eve's Children* when the actor declares, 'In this story I play the part of God. Please use your imaginations as freely as you wish.' More subtle, is the text of *Clever Else*. Here, the entire story is told in a kind of self-referential direct address. Everything is played out to the audience as large theatrical characters. The style is self-consciously theatrical and the audience relationship becomes one of collaborating in this theatricality.

   The following short pieces of dialogue can be used for you to play between the three styles. When am I an actor/narrator addressing the audience? When am I a character/narrator addressing the audience? When am I a character addressing other characters?

   The exercise is to play with the scenes in pairs and explore the possibilities of when to turn the scene out to the audience and when to turn in to the other character.

## Example A

**A**  Once there was a Queen (my part in this scene), she was angry and she paced up and down.

**B**  The King (who happens to be my thing), was sitting down eating his breakfast.

**A**  The Queen was furious, 'Must you slurp your porridge!'

**B**   'A slurp is better than a burp, my dear,' he said, wiping his mouth on his sleeve.

### Example B

**A**   A proud Princess was walking in the fields picking flowers, like this.

**B**   A wicked Goblin watched from afar, like this.

**A**   And when she placed her crown down on the ground . . .

**B**   He crept up on her and stole it away.

**A**   Put my crown down you little clown!

### Example C

**A**   Once there was a very stupid boy called Monty – he was stupid and he was ugly.

**B**   His sister, Tamara, was extremely clever and beautiful. I will swap you my shiny £1 coin for your tatty old £5 note.

**A**   Thank you very much! said Monty, feeling very pleased with himself.

**B**   My pleasure, said Tamara, exiting smugly, stage right.

## THE TALES: PERFORMANCE NOTES AND EXERCISES

### The Prologue

There is an implied sense of urgency and a call for the audience's attention in the words of the Prologue. These words can be delivered by one person or divided amongst the cast. They can be spoken all at once at the beginning or delivered/echoed in between each tale.

## Prologue Exercise

The cast of each tale chooses three or four dramatic moments from their story. Show these moments without words, giving a flavour of each tale. Then practise moving from one dramatic moment to another in small groups. Do not shuffle from one to another, but allow the movement to flow and so create a movement sequence which includes glimpses of these dramatic moments.

Now as the Prologue is spoken, feed in each group one at a time, so that the sequences fill the performance space, slightly overlapping each one. The effect should be as though the Prologue were conjuring up moments from the tales, or the audience is flicking through a book of tales to scan the illustrations prior to reading.

The final movement sequence should allow you to finish in your opening positions for the first tale to be told.

# Six Servants

Six Servants has the feel of The Magnificent Seven, or a collection of Marvel Comic heroes with super-powers, coming to save the day. Each servant is extremely proud of their talent. The marked contrast to this is Frosty-Hot who, apologetic for her presence amongst them, deflates their pronouncements of magnificence.

## Six Servants Exercise

A theatrical character can be identified through the use of a physical motif by the actor. A physical motif might be a slouched stance with hunched shoulders, the habit of winking at others, standing hands together with the tips of your fingers touching your chin or rising up and down on the balls of your feet. The motif says 'I'm like this' and provides the essence of the character for the audience. When playing in a stylised manner these motifs should be large and exaggerated, and used to punctuate particular moments in the play.

Find physical motifs for the characters in Six Servants. Experiment with different parts of the body and stances for each character. How would an evil queen hold her hands? Find the stance for a beautiful and wise princess, or the stoutest man in the world. Then find the points in the tale when the characters are saying 'I am like this' and incorporate the physical motifs into the performance.

## Clever Else

Play as much of this tale as you can to the audience, as everything is reported in the present tense – I am doing . . . I am saying . . . I am thinking . . . – as the character does so. Make eye contact with the audience and keep your body angle to them as a disciplined exercise. After the opening section, the sequence of events repeat themselves five times and can be punctuated by the players creating sounds, as each character carries out the same set of actions. This repeated rhythm includes the sounds of: descending the cellar steps, opening the cellar door, the sudden horror upon seeing the axe and the crying/wailing.

### Clever Else Exercise

Improvise a simple scene using the following stimuli as starting points:
1. Family breakfast
2. Taking an exam
3. A blind date
4. Chickens waiting to lay

Now repeat the situation, but this time report to the audience all you are saying, doing and thinking. For example, Improvisation 1 might begin: **A** 'I am sitting here wondering what is for breakfast'; **B** 'I am smelling something strange in the kitchen.'; **C** 'I am accidentally burning the toast!'

## The Old Woman and Her Granddaughter and The Stolen Pennies

Think about the rhythms within these two short stories. Playing two rhythms against each other can be used to dramatic effect, as can finding the right moment to speed-up or slow-down the rhythm of dialogue or action.

### Old Woman Exercise
Discuss and decide upon appropriate rhythms for:
1. The Grandmother's movements
2. The Girl playing
3. The anger of the parents

Is the rhythm fast/slow/steady/changing?
Practise tapping out a rhythm after each character has delivered dialogue from the scene.
Each actor tap out the appropriate rhythm for their character.

### Stolen Pennies Exercise
Now find a rhythm for:
1. The clock striking
2. The Ghost-Child walking
3. The Child digging into the floor

Again practise tapping out a rhythm as the dialogue is delivered.

You may have discovered two or three central rhythms to the scene. Some might be played once, some might come and go. Now apply this information to the dialogue, movement and sound of the scene.

## The Shoes That Were Danced Through
In finding the movement for this tale think about the King's possessiveness and authority, the way that the Princesses behave in front of him and behind his back, or when he is not present. There is also a marked contrast between the freedom of expression at their secret liaison and the thought that they may lose this freedom.

### Shoes Danced Through Exercise
When the Princesses are preparing themselves for their

underground party, decide upon specific actions for each one to engage in – putting on make-up, holding up dresses, brushing hair etc. Establish a waltz time – a count of 1–2–3, 1–2–3 – and practise completing or repeating the actions to this three-time count. The count should also take you from place to place or from action to action.

## Six Stupid Hans

In common with the other tales, but perhaps most marked here, Hans plays with rhythm and repetition. Following the initial introduction, a similar sequence plays six times. The challenge is not to play repetition until tedium sets in. When does the rhythm change? In what ways are the brothers different? How do the actions vary? As for the 'impossible' moments of staging – we don't have to see the action necessarily, but the effect of, or reaction to, the action can be enough. So it's not putting the goat down your trousers which is funny, but the way that you walk when it's down there.

### Six Stupid Hans Exercise

In the original production this tale was played with the characters as marionettes. You might not adopt this idea, but this exercise helps with blocking and focus.

Position the characters upon the stage, each one flopping over or in a heap as marionettes without taut strings. When the focus is on your character or they are active, you are 'pulled-up' by the invisible strings and move as a marionette. When the focus is off the character they return to the slumped position. This gives a clear indication of what we want to show the audience at each point in the tale, and by switching character on and off disposes with unnecessary exits and entrances.

## Eve's Children

There's handsome and there's handsome. There's ugly and there's ugly. How is your handsome character handsome in their own individual way? The scene plays upon the comedy between the two groups and their reaction to their different circumstances. However, the handsome ones can be revolting in their handsomeness and the uglies can be endearing in their ugliness. Good luck with the casting.

## Eve's Children Exercise

Here is another story where the physicality of each character must be bold and exaggerated. Playing with tableaux (frozen pictures) is one way to examine the physicality of the character or group of characters.

The tale can be divided into three sections and the following tableaux created for each:

1. Eve's introduction – 'six handsome ones … six ugly ones …'
Create three tableaux which introduce us to the handsomes and three for the ugly ones. Once you have three you like, run them in quick succession so that all characters move together and freeze together, as though we are seeing a slide show (e.g. 'six handsome ones … click – picture one, click – picture two, click – picture three, then repeat with the uglies)
2. Eve's instruction to the children
Find a frozen image for each of the actions given to the characters by Eve (e.g. combing hair, scraping bricks etc.). Now divide each action into three frozen pictures with a starting point, an action and a finishing point. Finally run this sequence as a slide show as before, or move quickly giving the effect of flicking pages of cartoon drawings to make movement.
3. God's blessing
Find proud and magnificent tableaux for each of the handsome blessings (mighty monarch etc.). Find disappointed and burdened tableaux for the ugly blessings (woodcutter etc.)

## Twelve Sisters

The Chorus lines can be played in a number of ways. They can be divided amongst the sisters and brother or delivered through a separate group of actors: the Chorus. In the latter case, the Chorus observes and comments to the audience upon the action. The Chorus members can help to create the changes in environment with their bodies and the performance materials, e.g. the move from the palace to the sisters running through the forest. The Chorus members might also aid the transformation into ravens by lifting and catching, or through the nature of their movement, e.g. as a group watching the ravens' line of flight across the sky.

**Twelve Sisters Exercise**

Play 'Granny's Footsteps' together. This is a game where one person (Granny) stands facing the wall and the others go to the opposite end of the room. The winner is the first one to creep up on Granny and touch her on the back. However, Granny can turn round at any point and if she sees you moving she says your name. You must then go back to your starting point at the end of the room. The group will naturally stop and start together when Granny turns round and turns back. They become a Chorus in their movement quality and rhythm.

Attempt to show this quality of movement from the game but without someone playing Granny. All focus on where Granny would be and silently creep together and stop together, all moving forward towards your point of focus. Don't look at each other, but use your peripheral vision. Now apply this sensitivity to the points of choral movement in the tale.

## CONTEXT NOTES FOR THE PERFORMER

### *Where do we see Grimms' Tales today?*

Jacob and Wilhelm Grimms' collection of over 200 tales is currently the most widely distributed book next to the Bible. Amongst the most well known of these stories are, Cinderella, Red Riding Hood, Hansel & Gretel, The Frog Prince, Rapunzel, Snow White and Sleeping Beauty. It might surprise you that your first experience of the theatre is likely to have been an encounter with Grimm. Look in the theatre listings of any national newspaper for December or January and there will not only be theatres providing the traditional fairy tale-based panto but others re-working a tale in a contemporary style. For example, during January 1999, 25 theatres in London and the South East alone were offering performances based upon Grimms' work. Aspects of the Grimms can be seen throughout our society: in film, dance, art, children's and adult books and as powerful tools of advertising.

The German brothers' first hand-written collection of stories dates from 1810, with printed publication coming in 1812. There then followed seven different editions or versions of the tales, the last in 1857.

## Why did the Grimms tell tales?

The Grimms' father died in 1796, leaving their mother with five sons and a daughter to bring up. The family budget was reduced greatly overnight and they were forced to move home. Jacob and Wilhelm, as the eldest brothers, became 'heads' of the household at only 11 and 9 years old. Letters to other relatives at the time show boys remarkably mature for their age with a real sense of responsibility for their family. Later, whilst they were students studying law together, their mother died. The loss of both parents cannot be underestimated regarding their search for traditional tales, which they began as students and continued throughout the rest of their lives. In many of their tales the central character must leave home and go on a journey to establish a new life for him/herself. Often this central character loses, disobeys, or is abandoned by, parents.

If we then consider their society, the Grimms were associated with the new bourgeois class, not peasants or land owners, but professionals seen by the Grimms as standing for a better life through hard work and bringing with it a new and better Germany. Germany at this time had been made insecure by war and the French occupation of their central states. The brothers' collection of German tales can be seen as their attempt to come to terms with losing their home life and to establish an identity and new way of living for their country — to resurrect the Father and the Fatherland.

## What does telling a tale tell about the teller?

If we take the specific example of the Grimms' story *Twelve Brothers*, we can see that their telling is clearly shaped to meet personal needs as it mirrors their own circumstances. Originally entitled *Twelve Brothers and A Little Sister*, the Grimms' family were five brothers and their little sister, Lotte.

The narrative of *Twelve Brothers and a Little Sister* unfolds as follows, mirroring the circumstances of the brothers Grimm:

- the father causes the loss of family life ➔ the Grimms' father dies when the brothers are young

- the mother attempts to keep the family together but eventually the children must find their own way and establish a home without their parents ➔ the Grimms' mother struggles on but dies when the brothers are students

- the children are saved through their dedication to each other. ➔ Wilhelm lived with Jacob until his death in 1859, Jacob's death coming only four years later.

The act of telling is revealing on many levels. In *Tales Untold* I have re-told *Twelve Brothers* as *Twelve Sisters*. Here the sisters dare to flee into the woods and learn to cope independently. Could this be a tale for my own three daughters? Be aware that when you choose to tell tales, they will tell us about you. Quite simply, such tales help us to work things through, and the telling of tales through performance allows us to do this together.

## Who made up the stories?

The Grimm brothers did not create the tales but collected them from various sources and then adapted them. The stories in the Grimm collection are not created by an author, as in the case of Hans Christian Anderson, but the brothers re-told tales which already existed.

So where did the stories come from? Some of the tales were already written down in other books, particularly French publications, and the brothers selected the ones which appealed to them. However, the majority were from the oral tradition, told in spoken form from person to person, changing slightly with each re-telling. The writing of *Tales Untold* was influenced by the fact that three of the central sources for the Grimms' collection are female. The brothers heard stories from:

i)  their sister Lotte's circle of friends, young women between the ages of 8 and 20

ii)  the author Annette von Droste-Hülshoff and friends in their 30s and 40s

iii)  the source most widely noted, Dorothea Viehmann in her 50s, who spent hours telling them tales in their own study.

It is Frau Viehmann whose portrait can be found in later editions of the Grimms' collection. This portrait would say to the reader: we have taken the tales straight from the 'Old Wife's mouth', so to speak.

Of the tales I have used which can be attributed to a specific source, Annette's sister, Jenny, provided *Shoes Danced Through* — a story with a strong female voice concerning rebellion against a father's authority, and Frau Viehmann provided *Twelve Brothers*, the basis for *Twelve Sisters* in this text. Other tales may have come from their sister and her friends, or from tellers unknown. The tales had been told and retold, passed down a line which stretches back to an untraceable point of their initial creation, and there would lie a different tale.

## What were the stories saying?

Identifying with a heroine, these female storytellers retained in their memory and chose to tell those tales where the female is central to the story. Therefore many of the original tales began quite promisingly for the woman or the girl, but by the end of Jacob and Wilhelm's version she is put in her place, under the rule of the male figure of authority. Later, in the mid 20th-century, this fatherly hand of the Grimms is replaced by the firm macho grip of Disney's version of the stories, as the prince becomes an all-action hero coming to the rescue of the poor unfortunate female. Though central to the original tale the woman struggles to retain control.

The way the women originally told these tales as spoken to the Grimms has obviously been lost to us, but there are clues to changes made by the Grimms when we look at the different editions of their collection. From the 1812 edition to the 1819 edition Cinderella becomes more and more silent, and less and less active in moving her story forward. On the other hand, the wicked stepmother has more and more evil statements to make, so that by the later editions the message of Cinderella is clearly that female talk equals wickedness. In Hansel and Gretel the father's role in abandoning the children is steadily decreased and greater emphasis placed upon the step-mother in edition after edition. Snow White's list of housework increases until she must cook, sew, knit, make the beds, tidy and clean for the dwarfs and make sure the dinner is ready when they return from work!

The Grimms used the stories to meet their own needs and to emphasise their own ideas regarding class, leaving an old way of life and finding a new one, and, in the examples above, the role of men and women.

Disney's telling of the Grimms' tales celebrates male power (the role of the male hero in the cartoon adaptations is increased enormously) and evil is presented as a female out of control – the Queen in Snow White, the Witch in Sleeping Beauty, the Step-Mother in Cinderella.

## Can we change stories?

For both book and film the tale is fixed and will always be read or seen as the same story. In the oral tradition, where the tale has been passed from person to person by word of mouth, tales may be told in many ways, but still thought of as the same story.

The medium of the theatre is the nearest that we have to the spoken storytelling tradition in our modern society; it allows for the constant flow of communication between sender (the actor) and receiver (the audience). Dramatising the tales in the collection can teach us about the particular nature of live performance – a simultaneous sharing in the creation of a story which cannot be fixed. Rather, the very nature of performance is concerned with a continuously changing story. The telling of these Tales Untold has received contributions from the Grimms, various translators, and myself as author of the stimulus text. Now, as you tell the tales, you too contribute to their telling, and the way your audience will receive them should add to this line of changes to the tales. No two performance groups will tell them in exactly the same way. The changes that you or I make to the tales are an attempt to tell it how it *is*, not how it *was*.

## How can we tell these tales?

In performing Tales Untold there are lots of decisions you must make as storytellers. There are 'impossible' staging moments throughout: when Stout expands to three thousand times his size, when Hans pulls out his own eye, when the sisters turn into ravens and fly away over the tree tops. If you attempt to literally create these moments by a great theatrical illusion or effect, you take up the position of 'fooling' the audience, and their response is often to work out how the trick is done, the story is forgotten, and to a certain extent the performers and audience are set against each other. Expertly executed mime is equally distracting as the performer becomes 'clever' in showing their expertise or, alternatively, confuses due to a lack of ability. Therefore, in attempting to show the entire Red Sea being swallowed or the disappearance of the ghost-child, or Hans placing a goat down his own trousers, use bodies and a few simple props to say 'what happened was a bit like this'. The little bit suggested asks for the support of the audience in the effect created, placing them upon more equal terms as together you create the 'impossible' moment – The *Shoes Danced Through* text becomes a stimulus for movement ideas, and lines are not assigned to characters; *The Six Servants* requests the fantastical to be represented, including the shattering of a fly into a thousand pieces; *Six Stupid Hans* require a goat, a hog, dogs and pigs. Each story has very specific problems to solve, and there are no prescribed solutions. The telling of the tale belongs to you.

## THE ORIGINAL TALES

The most comprehensive collection, containing the most engaging telling of the original tales I have come across, is:
Ralph Manheim's translation of *Grimms' Tales for Young and Old*, Gollanz, 1993
There are numerous other collections, including:
*The Complete Grimms' Fairy Tales* (introduced by Padriac Colum), Routledge & Kegan Paul, 1975
*Brothers Grimm, Popular Folk Tales* (translated by Brian Alderton), Gollanz, 1996
*Tales From Grimm* (freely translated by Wanda Gagg), Faber & Faber, 1937